GET TO KNOW CLASSICAL MASTERPIECES

Ludwig van Beethoven

(1770–1827)

Symphony No. 5

in C minor op. 67

In a simple arrangement for piano
by Hans-Günter Heumann

Drawings by Brigitte Smith

ED 21047

ISMN 979-0-001-17574-6

SCHOTT

Mainz · London · Berlin · Madrid · New York · Paris · Prague · Tokyo · Toronto

© 2011 SCHOTT MUSIC GmbH & Co. KG, Mainz · Printed in Germany

Dear Pianists,

In this volume you will find a simple piano arrangement of Symphony No. 5 in C minor op. 67 by Ludwig van Beethoven (1770–1827). This arrangement of one of the greatest and best-known works in classical music is designed to provide an introduction to the work, presenting its main themes in easily playable form. The enormous range of this symphony means that it has not been possible to reproduce all the movements in their entirety: in the second movement, for example, I have concentrated on the theme and the first variation. For more detailed study of the work I recommend listening with the Eulenburg score (Schott EAS 115), which even comes with a CD.

This symphony has also become known as the 'Fate Symphony', owing to a motif identified by Anton Schindler, Beethoven's secretary and first biographer. According to Schindler, Beethoven said of the four-note motif that opens the first movement: '*Thus Fate knocks at the door*'. This motif dominates the Fifth Symphony and has become almost a musical symbol for Beethoven.

This inexorable hammering represents the struggle with destiny, a theme that runs through Beethoven's life. In 1802 he wrote a letter of farewell to his brothers, known as the Heiligenstadt testament, in which he expressed the torment of his increasing deafness. It begins with the words: '*Oh you men who think or say that I am malevolent, stubborn or misanthropic, how greatly do you wrong me...*' It goes on: '*Oh, how harshly was I then cast out by the doubly sad experience of my bad hearing...*'

No listener can resist the power of this symphony as it draws them in to feel and participate in the eternal human struggle through suffering and redemption, culminating in triumph.

And now let yourselves be enchanted by the unique qualities of this work.

With best wishes,
Hans-Günter Heumann

Contents

Biography of the Composer Ludwig van Beethoven

1770:   christened in Bonn on 17 December; probably born on 16 December. Little Ludwig showed enormous early musical talent and had his first lessons with his father, later studying with various musicians in Bonn.

1778:   At a concert in Cologne Beethoven's father presented his son as a child prodigy, rather like Mozart.

1780:   took lessons with the Bonn court organist Christian Gottlob Neefe.

1783:   employed as accompanist (on the harpsichord or organ) in the court orchestra.

1784:   appointed assistant court organist by Prince Maximilian Franz.

1787:   granted leave of absence by the Prince to take lessons from Mozart in Vienna. The sudden death of Beethoven's mother meant he had to return to Bonn to look after his two younger brothers, though, as their father was an alcoholic.

1792:   Beethoven moved to Vienna. He immersed himself in study and worked as a piano teacher, pianist and composer. He was highly regarded as a pianist and composer by members of the Viennese establishment who provided him with financial support.

1795:   first public concert featuring Beethoven's own works at the *Burgtheater* in Vienna. First signs of deafness that became progressively worse with age.

1802:   the 'Heiligenstadt testament' reflected the extent of his suffering.

after 1818:   he could only communicate by writing in 'conversation books'.

1827:   Beethoven died in Vienna on 26 March. His funeral was attended by tens of thousands of mourners and onlookers. Franz Schubert was among the torchbearers.

History of the work:
Symphony No. 5 in C minor op. 67

Four movements (*Allegro con brio – Andante con moto – Allegro – Allegro*)

Structure: 1st movement: Sonata form – exposition (introduction of themes), development (exploration of the themes) and reprise (restatement of themes).

2nd movement: theme with variations

3rd movement: *scherzo*, commonly used since Beethoven instead of the minuet

4th movement: *finale* in the form of a march – a song of jubilation in contrast with the darkly dramatic minor key of the first movement.

Dedicated to Prince Franz Joseph von Lobkovitz and Count Andrey Kirillovich Razumovsky.

Beethoven worked on the fifth Symphony for a long time, beginning as early as 1803 and not completing it until 1808. This was because he was working on several projects at once at the time.

First performed on 22 December 1808, conducted by Beethoven in a programme including his 'Pastoral' Symphony No. 6 in F major op. 68, Piano Concerto No. 4 in G major op. 58, parts of the Mass in C major op. 86 and the Fantasie in C minor op. 80 for piano, choir and orchestra.

Orchestration: 2 flutes, 1 piccolo, 2 oboes, 2 clarinets, 2 bassoons, 1 contrabassoon, 2 horns, 2 trumpets, 3 trombones, timpani, strings

1st Movement

Ludwig van Beethoven
1770–1827

Allegro con brio ♩ = 96

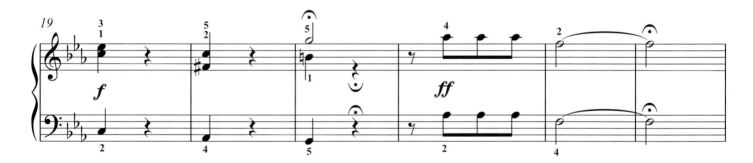

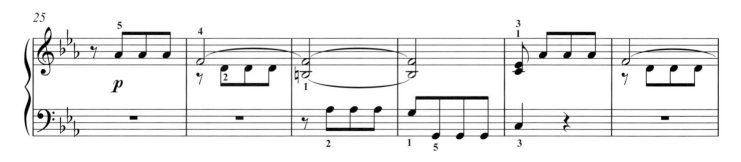

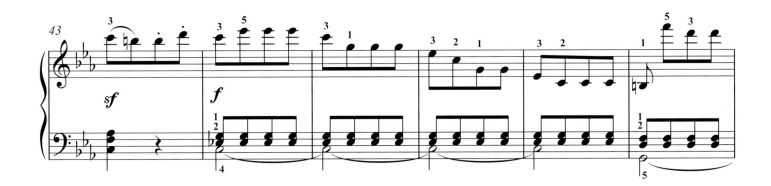

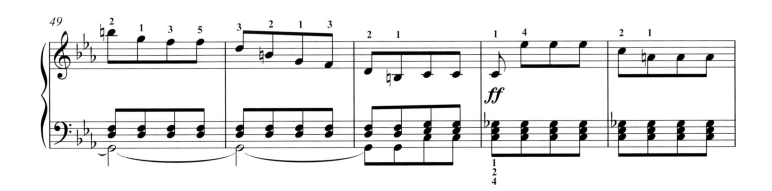

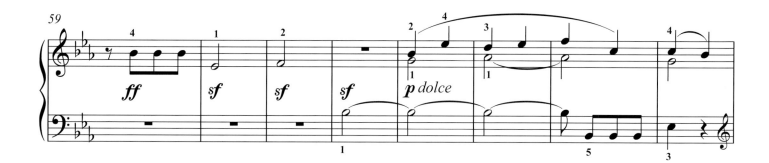

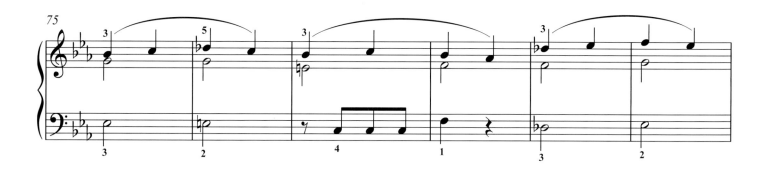

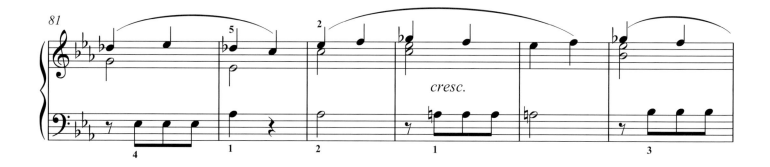

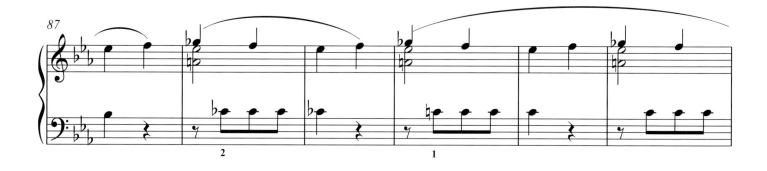

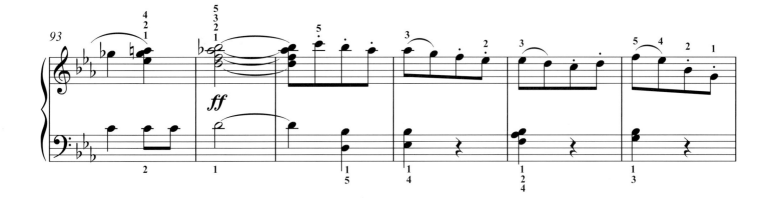

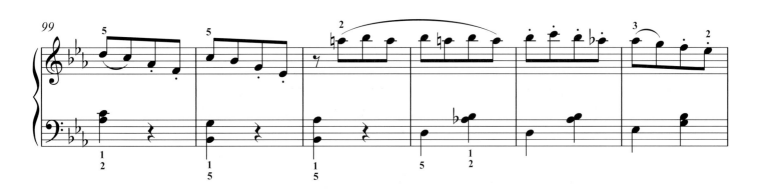

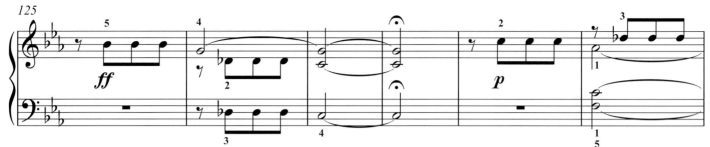

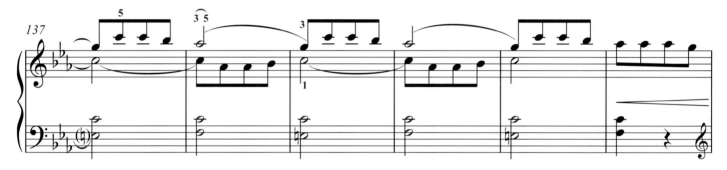

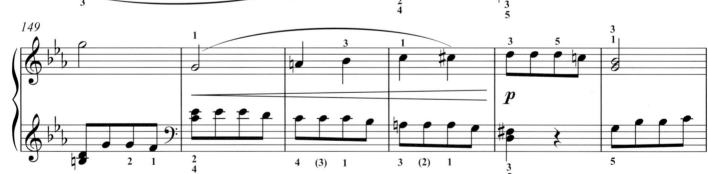

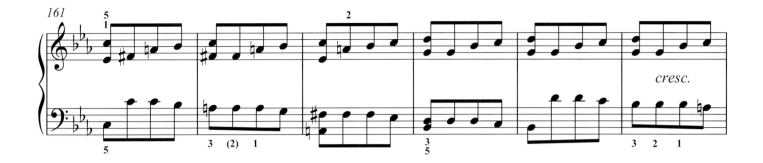

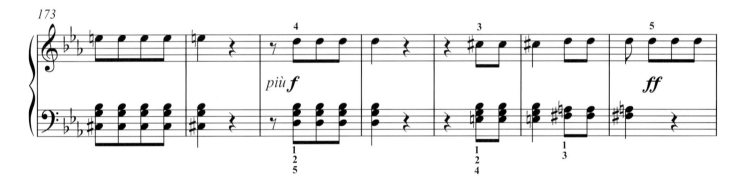

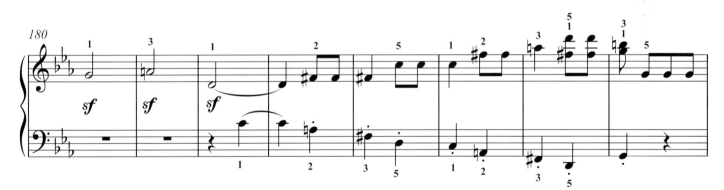

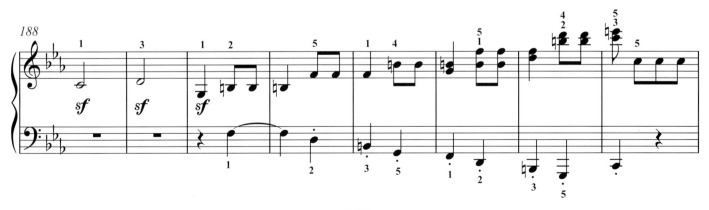

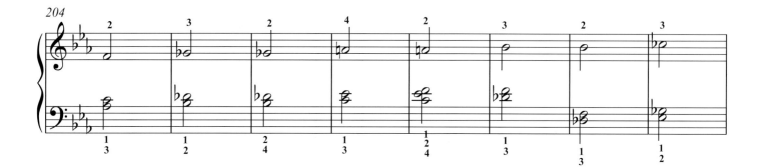

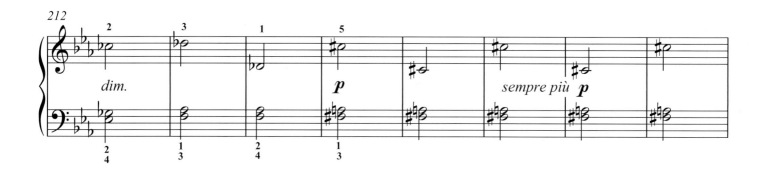

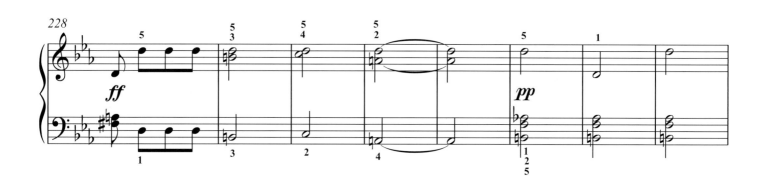

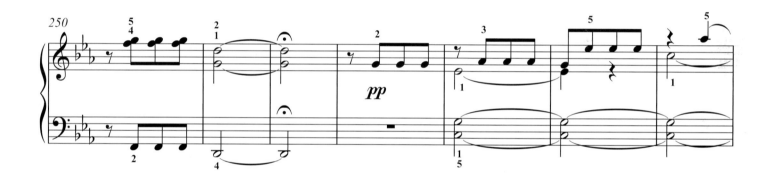

2nd Movement

Andante con moto ♩ = 92

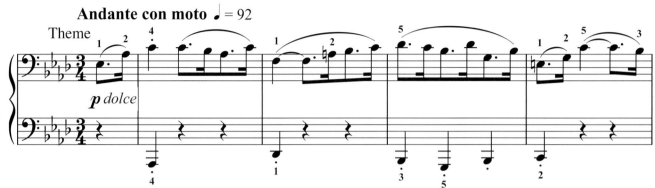

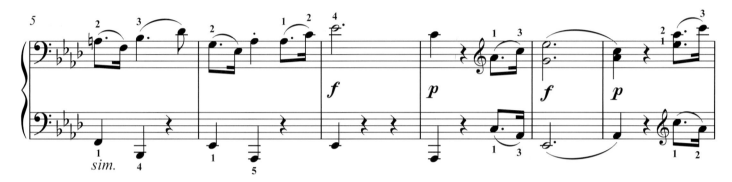

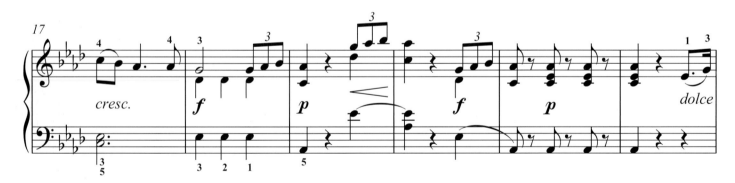

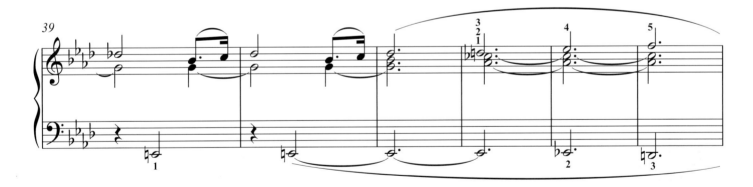

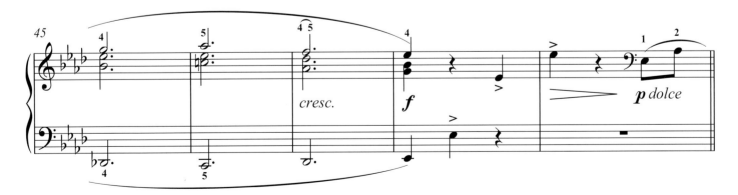

1st Variation

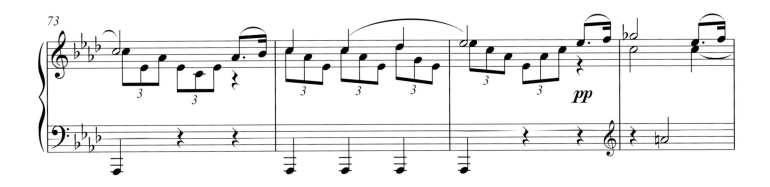

3rd Movement

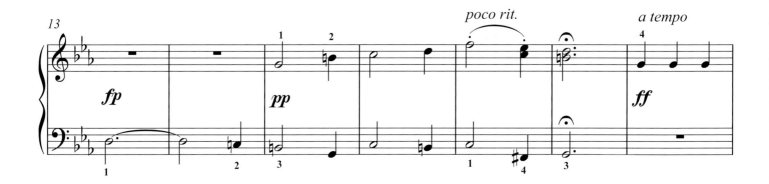

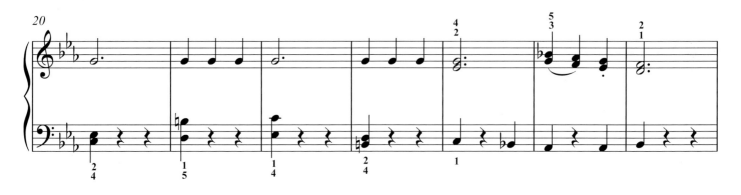

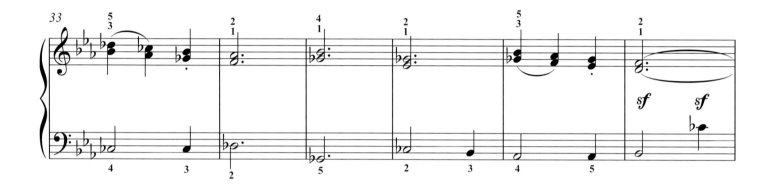

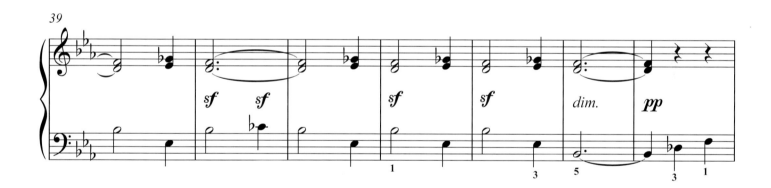

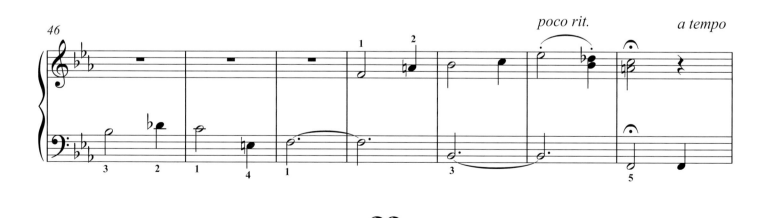

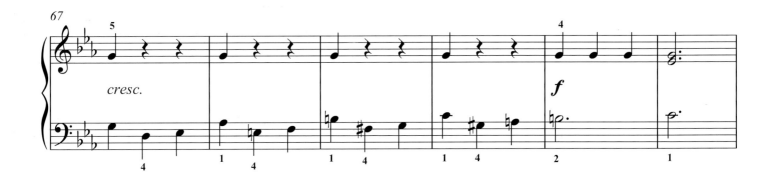

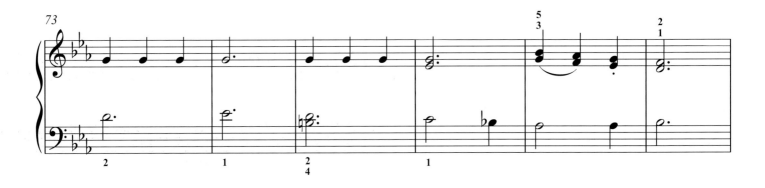

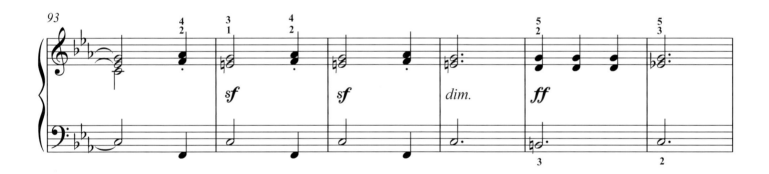

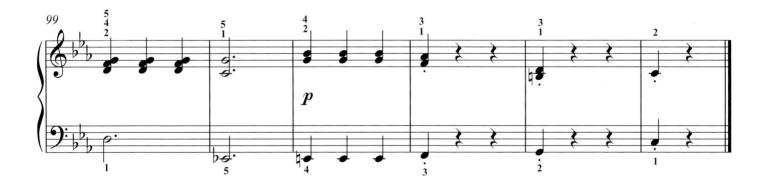

4ᵗʰ Movement

Allegro ♩ = 84

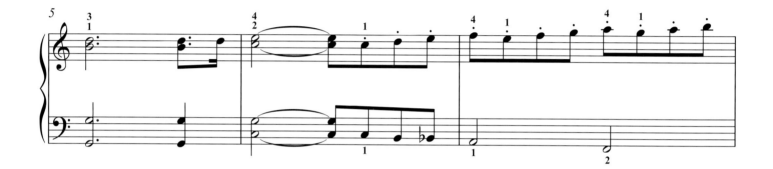

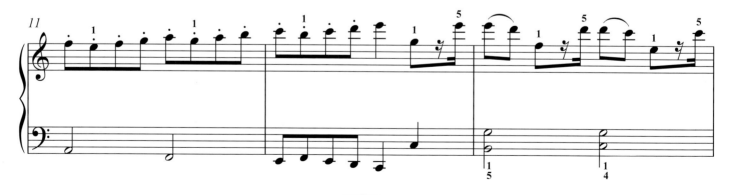

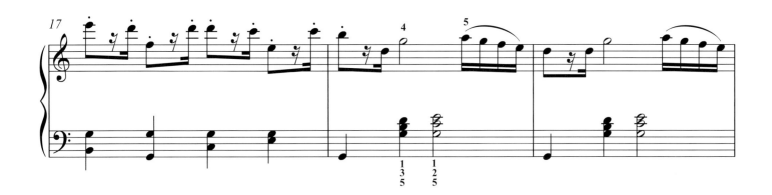

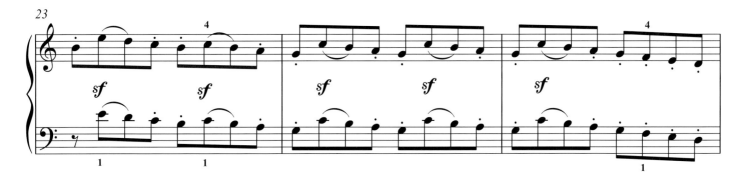

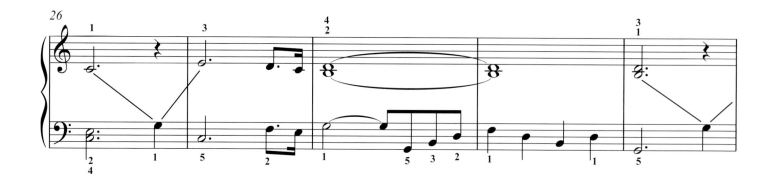

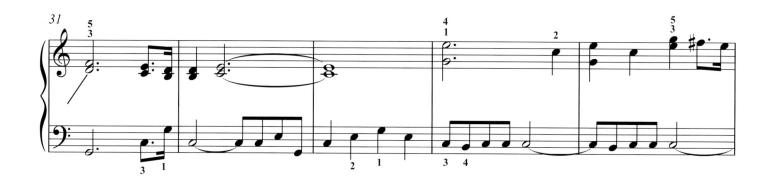

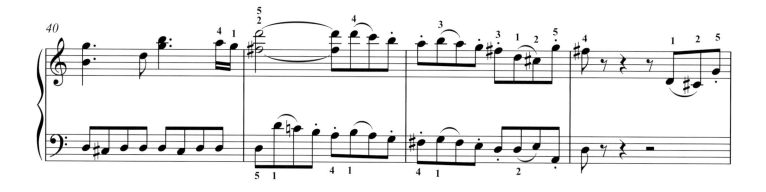

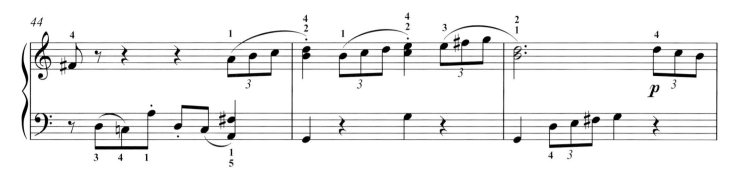

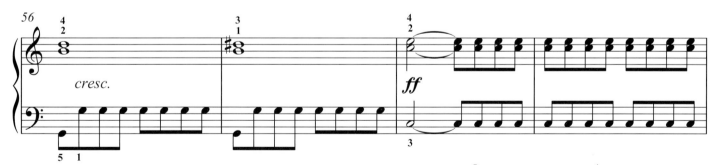

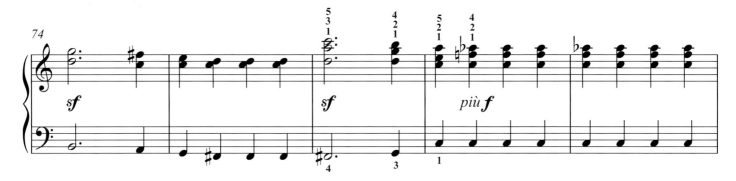

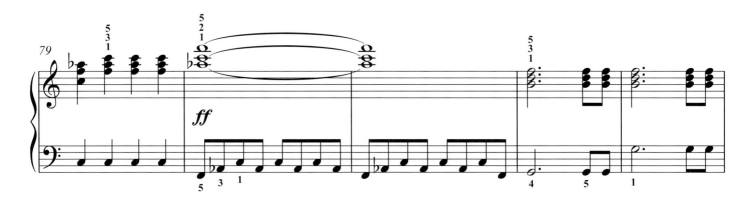

Schott Music, Mainz 54 230